A Mother's Poem To Her Son
A View Into Children's Lives
Through Parents' Eyes

Written by Bob Johnson
Illustrated by Inger Johnson

ISBN: 978-0-9826036-0-4
Cataloguing in publication data is on file with the Library of Congress
Visit us on our website: www.keepsake-books.com   www.bobinlou.com

It was a day
like no other would be.
I became a mother to you,
and you a son to me.

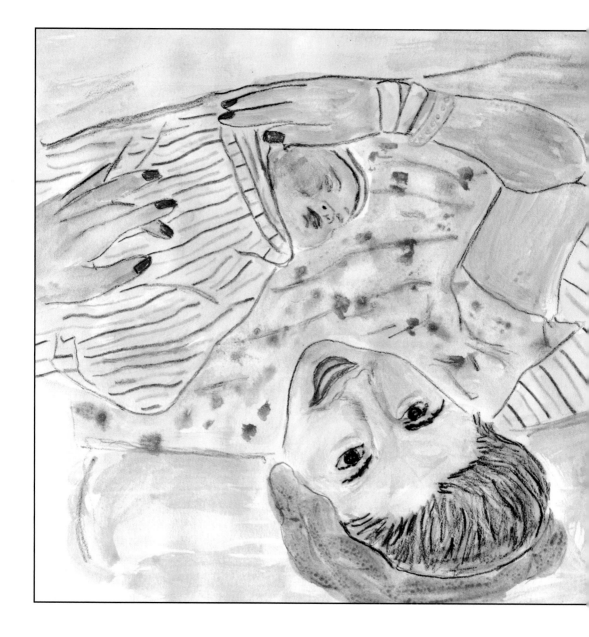

The feeling I felt at your birth was the only one like it on my God's earth. It touched my soul in a place virgin and wild; saved only for a woman's just born child.

Time seems to be in such a rush with me. First you were one, then two and now three. You taught me that time can be only God driven, and that you, son, are a gift God given.

You'll soon be four, and now Mom's pup wants his own pup, and asks Mom, "Mom, when can we pick my pup up?" I know I will feed it, water it, walk it, and pick up poo, but there's just so much joy in hearing my boy, "Mom, those are all things I know how to do."

Then will come five and off to half-day school to learn that not all apply the golden rule. You'll learn, and far too young, that there are those that just don't care, and can't and don't and won't ever play fair.

By six you will have sorted
through all the "school rules"
like life, no matter the age,
simply put, suffers no fools.
And that life's path, from its
beginning to end, is much easier
walked with the hand of a friend.

Then comes seven and you'll say with question and pause, "Mom, do you know for sure there is a Santa Claus?" And I'll tell you, "I know it's true and yes, you bet I do;" then go in the other room, sigh - and think about how fast time has gone by.

Out of nowhere comes eight
years of age and it's time
to turn one more life page.
Baseball, golf, tennis and
swimming, and all of the lessons
taught by losing and winning.

By nine and the start of fourth grade, your debt to school years one, two, and three will all have been paid. And, after long nights and so much discussion with Mom and Pop, you'll understand that it's integrity, and ethics, and morals, and taking a stand that make a good man.

You'll want to skip ten and go straight to eleven. You'll ask philosophical questions like, "Mom, is there a God? Is there a Heaven?" I'll tell you, "It's okay just to hope so, and then to pray until you know."

And now twelve, thirteen and fourteen and middle school... "Mom, I think girls might really be cool." And now another talk late into the night about the consequences of not doing right.

And then the confusion of high school and applying all your life's learned rules, but now with some choice and a listened to voice.

Now time to be off to a university and God knows you've earned it. For twelve years now, if they taught it, you learned it. You've done well in high school and on SAT tests. And you've seen life's hard work rewards only the best.

Another graduation – I know it seems so long to you, but not so for me, since that day like no other would be. Now, all on your own, you're starting your life. You just called and you're taking a wife.

We just spoke again today.
Your first child is on its way.
"Mom, that question I asked
when I was only eleven –
I know now there is a God
and there is a Heaven."

And you'll truly understand what I, your grandmothers and theirs before them know and knew: just how and when to tighten the screw. And that the strongest and longest most binding of things, are family ties and heart strings.

I want you to know whether infant, child, adolescent or man, whether in fact or in heart, I'll always be there to hold your hand. And that all that we've had was God given, and it's God's will that life is for livin'.

Books in this series:

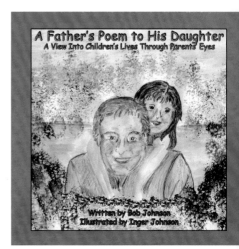

www.keepsake-books.com

www.bobinlou.com